FREE S FOR KIDS

The Third Edition

Director: Bruce Lansky
Executive Editor: Kathe Grooms
Editor: Tom Grady
Art Director: Tom Oberg
Asst. Art Director: Marcia Conley

OUR PLEDGE

We have collected the best free and up-to-a-dollar offers that we could find. We have examined every single item. We don't think you'll be disappointed when you send away for things (though mistakes do happen) because every supplier of items in this book has promised, in writing, to honor single requests through 1980 — and beyond, as long as supplies last.

Meadowbrook Press
Wayzata, Minnesota 55391

DEDICATION

To **Pat Blakely, Barbara Haislet,** and **Judith Hentges** for creating and publishing the original Rainbow Book, and for proving that children, parents and teachers would respond enthusiastically to a source of free things by mail. They taught us the importance of carefully checking the quality of each item and of doing our best to make sure that each and every child's request is satisfied.

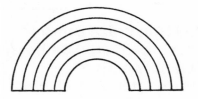

Fifth Printing February, 1980

PRINTED IN THE UNITED STATES OF AMERICA
ISBN 0-915658-12-7
Copyright © 1976, 1977, 1979
© Revised edition 1979 by Meadowbrook Press

what's inside

CONTENTS

🐰 = especially for younger kids

🐻 = especially for older kids

about this book

FREE STUFF FOR KIDS contains over 250 listings of things that children can send away for. We think the items in this book are the best free offers available to children. You will not find any "trick" offers — only wholesome, safe, fun and informative things we know kids like!

In this day of rising costs it is not surprising that some items require a small fee or a self-addressed, stamped envelope. In this edition, we have allowed fees of up to but no more than $1.00.

We have examined every item in this book. Each supplier of items has agreed in writing to honor single requests through 1980 — and beyond, as long as supplies last.

The book is designed especially for independent use by children who can read and write. General directions in the introductory chapter tell exactly how to send a request. Mailing instructions for each item are clear and consistent. Half the fun is knowing you can use the book entirely on your own!

The other half is getting a real reward for your efforts!

Our heartfelt appreciation goes to the hundreds of corporations, agencies and institutions for their cooperation in making this book possible. We also want to thank the dozens of children who have sent us their own ideas for FREE STUFF. The suppliers and the editors of this book have a common goal — to make it possible for children to reach out and discover the world by themselves.

USING THIS BOOK

using this book

working with this book

Before you start sending away for free stuff, get your book in shape. Fold it open, working your way from the two ends toward the middle. That will make the book lie flat while you read or copy addresses.

reading carefully

Read the descriptions carefully so you will know exactly what you are getting. Is it a folder or a booklet? A map or a poster? A comic book or a magazine reprint? (See the Index, page 111, for details.)

following directions

Be sure to follow the directions under each thing you send for. Most of the time the directions will tell you to use a postcard. Sometimes you will need to use paper and envelopes.

sending postcards

Make sure you use a postcard that's at least 3½ inches wide and 5½ inches long. (The post office won't accept 3-inch by 5-inch cards.)
Your postcard should look like this. The date, the request and your address are on one side. The company's address and the stamp are on the other side.

Jessie Rogers
Box 579 Star Route
Solon Springs, WI 54873

Director Corporate Services
International Salt Co.
Clarks Summit, PA 18411

Dear Sir or Madam:
    Please send me a copy of the Sterling Salt Fun fold-out.
    Thank you very much

            Sincerely yours,
            Jessie Rogers

sending letters

Your letters should look like this one. If you are including coins or a return envelope, say so in the letter.

Jessie Rogers
Box 579 Star Route
Solon Springs, WI 54873

Estes Industries
P. O. Box 227 Dept. 94
Penrose, CO 81240

Box 579 Star Route
Solon Springs, WI 54873
January 30, 1980

Dear Sir or Madam:

Please send me a copy of the Alpha Book of Model Rocketry and The Estes Catalog. I have enclosed 50¢ for postage and handling.
Thank you very much.

Sincerely yours,
Jessie Rogers

Ask for only one copy.
Print the name of the thing you want exactly as you see it in the directions.
Print the complete address of the company exactly as you see it in the directions.
Print your own name, street, city, state and zip code very carefully.

sending money

If the directions say to send in money for postage and handling, it's best to tape the coin (or coins) to your letter so they won't break out of your envelope.

sending a long envelope

If the directions say to send in a long, self-addressed, stamped envelope, here's how you do it. First address a 9" envelope to yourself. Put a first-class stamp on it. Then fold it up and put it inside another 9" envelope with your letter. Finally, address the second envelope to the company and put a first-class stamp on it.

stamps

You can buy postcards with the stamp already printed on them at your post office. You must put a first-class stamp on envelopes. Is the stamp glued on tight and the envelope well sealed?

double checking

Did you follow all the directions for the things you want?
Did you print the exact names of the things you want?
Is your own address complete and correct?
Is the company's whole address on your card or
    envelope?
Is your printing neat enough to read? (Ask a friend to
    read it back to you if you aren't sure.)
Don't forget to mail your cards and letters!

waiting

You should expect to wait 4 to 8 weeks for your things to arrive. We know it is a long time to wait. But if your things come sooner (and many of them will), then it will be a nice surprise.

how to make sure you get what you send for

We've tried to make the directions for using this book as clear as possible, because we want you to get what you send for. But you must follow **all** the instructions exactly as they're written on each page. If you don't, it's possible that the supplier will not be able to answer your request.

Here's a list of things to remember when asking for free stuff.

- **Do not** ask for more than **one** copy of an item.

- **Do** print your name and address clearly on the envelope **and** on the letter you send. Sometimes envelopes and letters get separated from one another.

- **Do** send all of the money asked for.

- **Do not** send pennies.

- **Do** tape the coins you send to the letter you send them with. If you don't, the money may rip the envelope and fall out.

- **Do** send a 9-inch long self-addressed, stamped envelope if instructions say to.

- **Do not** ask Meadowbrook Press to send you any of the items described in the book. We don't have supplies of them.

We don't want you to be disappointed, so please follow these rules.

MEADOWBROOK PRESS

FREE STUFF
FOR KIDS

7

HAVING FUN

yo-yo trickery

The DUNCAN yo-yo makers have a colorful booklet of yo-yo tricks to help make you an expert. It starts with easy ones like The Sleeper and quickly gets into more advanced ones like Double or Nothing — 36 tricks in all!

directions: Use paper and an envelope. You must send in $1.00.

ask for: DUNCAN YO-YOLYMPICS Booklet

write to: DUNCAN
P.O. Box 165
Baraboo, WI 53913

all stars

The All-Star Game brings together the greatest stars in Major League baseball. The 1980 game, the first ever played in Dodger Stadium, is commemorated in a 3-inch full-color emblem that you can send for.

directions: Use a postcard.

ask for: All-Star Game Logo

write to: All-Star Logo
Dodger Public Relations
Dodger Stadium
Los Angeles, CA 90012

skate skillfully

Roller skating is a lot of fun and it's easy to learn.
Send for a 10-page comic book that describes the
basic "Skating Skills." You can also learn about
fancy roller skating tricks, spins, games and dances
in an 11-page pamphlet.

directions: Use paper and an envelope. You
must send in 25¢ for **each** booklet.

ask for: Skating Skills
How to Roller Skate and Have Fun

write to: Chicago Roller Skate Co.
4458 W. Lake St.
Chicago, IL 60624

basketball history

Basketball is the only major sport founded in the United States. Order your basketball pamphlets to find out more facts.

directions: Use paper and a long envelope. You must enclose a long, self-addressed, stamped envelope.

ask for: Basketball Was Born Here
Basketball Hall of Fame

write to: Basketball Hall of Fame
Box 175 M, Highland Station
Springfield, MA 01109

helmets, helmets, helmets

Are you aware of all the different designs and colors used on the helmets of the various National Football League teams? Send for this colorful brochure and see the helmets of the 28 NFL teams.

directions: Use a postcard.

ask for: NFL Helmet Brochure

write to: The National Football League
410 Park Avenue
New York, NY 10022

bowling tips

You love to go bowling with your friends, right? But do you know how to score, how to throw a strike and how to convert a spare? This folder gives directions and helpful drawings so you'll have more fun bowling!

directions: Use paper and a long envelope. You must enclose a long, self-addressed, stamped envelope.

ask for: Tips for Junior Bowlers

write to: American Junior Bowling Congress
5301 S. 76th St.
Greendale, WI 53129

how to bowl

The ball glides down the alley, straight over the arrows and right into the pins! **Strike!** You did it — but how do you score it? Send for a pamphlet on bowling tips and find out. Start bowling like the pro's!

directions: Use a postcard.

ask for: Tips for Better Bowling
AMF Personal Bowling Score
  Record

write to: John Mazey
AMF Bowling
Jericho Turnpike
Westbury, NY 11590

12
SPORTS

can you canoe?

If you can't, you can find out how by sending for these four booklets. One gives a list of the schools that teach you how to canoe. One gives a list of the places in each state to rent canoes. The third one gives you a list of over 75 books about canoeing with helpful comments about each one. The last booklet is a guide to camping by canoe. It tells you how to pick a route, how to get organized, how to get in shape, what gear and food you'll need and much much more.

directions: Use paper and an envelope. You must send in 50¢ for **each** booklet. Say which booklet(s) you'd like.

ask for: Learn-To-Canoe Directory
Rent-A-Canoe Directory
The Grumman Book Rack
Group-Camping by Canoe

write to: Grumman Boats-Dept. WR
Grumman Allied Industries
Marathon, NY 13803

fishing guide

Do you love to fish? Then you'll love the new Mepps Fisherman's Guide. The large, 35-page booklet is filled with short stories about real fishermen (and fisher-kids) and the outstanding fish they caught — with color photos to prove them! The Guide includes new fishing tips. It shows all the famous Mepps lures. And it even tells you how you can enter the Junior Division of the Field and Stream Fish Contest!

directions: Use paper and an envelope. You must send in 25¢.

ask for: Mepps Fisherman's Guide

write to: Sheldons', Inc.
Box 508
Dept. K
Antigo, WI 54409

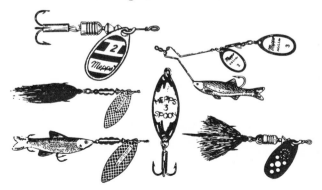

the rules of the game

Do you know what a deadball serve is in racquetball? How do you score a table tennis match? And what do you do when your golf ball goes out of bounds? Send away for the rules of the games you're interested in.

directions:	Use a postcard if the booklet is free. If there is a fee, use paper and an envelope and enclose the appropriate amount of money.
ask for:	Guide to Better Racquetball
write to:	Ektelon Dept. FS 8929 Aero Dr. San Diego, CA 92123
ask for:	Official Rules of Table Tennis (50¢)
write to:	U.S. Table Tennis Assn. 3466 Bridgeland Dr., Suite 209 St. Louis, MO 63044
ask for:	The Rules of Golf (50¢)
write to:	U.S. Golf Association Golf House Far Hills, NJ 07931

the olympic games

You'll be an expert about the Olympics if you send away for this 20-page booklet. It traces the fascinating history of these games from ancient times to the present day.

directions: Use a postcard.

ask for: The Olympic Games

write to: United States Olympic Committee
1750 East Boulder St.
Colorado Springs, CO 80809

table tennis tips

Some think that table tennis is the fastest racket sport there is. It's a quick, exciting game that's easy to begin playing, difficult to master, and a lot of fun to learn. Read about the game's history and pick up some tips for beginners in this booklet from the U.S. Table Tennis Association.

directions: Use paper and an envelope. You must send in 25¢.

ask for: Table Tennis for Everyone

write to: U.S. Table Tennis Assn.
3466 Bridgeland Dr., Suite 209
St. Louis, MO 63044

bike excitement

If you like bikes and bike racing, you'll love these two treats from Huffy. Send for a nifty 2x3-inch cloth patch to sew on your jeans or jacket. It shows two racers pedaling their bikes. You can also get a large, 20x27-inch poster that pictures three BMX (motor-cross) bike riders decked out in their racing gear.

directions: Use paper and an envelope. You must enclose 25¢ for **each** item you order, but you don't have to get both.

ask for: Cloth Bike Patch (25¢)
Takin It to the Max Poster (25¢)

write to: Advertising
Huffy Corporation
P.O. Box 1204
Dayton, OH 45401

batter up!

How would you like the autograph of your favorite baseball player? Whether you're an American League or a National League fan, you'll find one of your heroes listed below. Each autograph comes inscribed on a miniature wooden replica of the famous Louisville Slugger bat!

directions: Use paper and an envelope. You must send in 50¢ for **each** bat that you order.

ask for: Any of the following autographed bats.
Johnny Bench
Fred Lynn
Steve Garvey
George Foster
Pete Rose
Rod Carew
George Brett

write to: H & B Promotions
P.O. Box 18177 - Dept. RB
Louisville, KY 40218

christmas decorations

Most dough is mixed and baked and popped into your mouth. This dough is mixed and baked — and hung on your Christmas tree! It's salt sculpture from Morton Salt. A colorful pamphlet gives you the basic instructions.

directions:	Use a postcard.
ask for:	Dough-It-Yourself Christmas Decorations
write to:	Salt Sculpture Pamphlet Morton Salt Consumer Affairs Dept. 110 N. Wacker Dr. Chicago, IL 60606

easter egg ideas

Do you like to decorate eggs at Eastertime? You can send for a booklet of creative things to make from eggs and egg shells. It has ideas for a happy Easter party!

directions:	Use a postcard.
ask for:	PAAS Easter Egg Decorating and Party Ideas
write to:	PAAS Dept. RB Plough, Inc. P.O. Box 377 Memphis, TN 38151

move over, michelangelo!

Did you know you can make your own Play Clay from baking soda, cornstarch and water? You can, if you order this colorful folder. It shows how to shape it into almost anything — buttons and bowls, candlesticks and Christmas ornaments. Play Clay hardens just like real sculptor's clay. So move over Michelangelo!

directions: Use paper and a long envelope. You must enclose a long, stamped, self-addressed envelope.

ask for: Move Over Michelangelo

write to: Arm & Hammer
P.O. Box 369
Dept. PC - F
Piscataway, NJ 08854

20
CRAFTS

clay play

This 4-page pamphlet shows you how to make a basic play clay out of corn starch, baking soda and water. Then you can learn to vary that recipe using salt and even sand. Learn to make ornaments, decorations, jewelry and toys!

directions: Use a postcard.

ask for: Play Clay Play

write to: Play Clay Play
Dept. PC-FS
Box 307
Coventry, CT 06238

do it with glue

You can make a moldable dough out of glue, corn starch and flour. Shape it into all sorts of animals, ornaments and decorations. Then, surprise! It hardens overnight and you don't have to bake it. This colorful foldout shows you what to do.

directions: Use paper and a long envelope. You must enclose a long, stamped, self-addressed envelope.

ask for: Glue Dough/Glue Paint Booklet

write to: Glue Dough/Glue Paint Booklet
P.O. Box 157
Hilliard, OH 43026

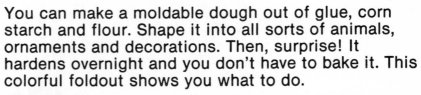

catalog of crafts kits

This colorful 144-page catalog of crafts kits is full of sources for beginners' kits in string art, latchhook, macrame, wood burning, candle making, glass staining and many more crafts.

directions: Use paper and an envelope. You must send in 25¢.

ask for: American Handicrafts/Merribee Needlearts Catalog

write to: American Handicrafts/Merribee Needlearts
P.O. Box 791
Dept. FSK
Fort Worth, TX 76101

when glue won't do

You can use a stapler when ordinary glue won't do the job. You'll find lots of easy projects with staples in two folders from Swingline.

directions: Use paper and a long envelope. You must enclose a long, stamped, self-addressed envelope.

ask for: Staple Fun
Staple Fun No. 2

write to: Swingline Company
Staple Fun
32-00 Skillman Ave.
Long Island City, NY 11101

be a reader leader!

EBONY JR! Magazine can bring you many fun-filled days of discovery. Join Sunny and Honey as they lead the way. You'll meet new friends from all over the world. Every issue is packed with sensational stories, great games, cartoons, and information about proud Black leaders of yesterday, today and tomorrow. Send for your own sample copy and get a world full of fun!

directions: Use paper and an envelope. You must send in 50¢. (No stamps please.)

ask for: One free copy of EBONY JR!

write to: EBONY JR! Magazine
Sunny and Honey
820 S. Michigan Ave.
Chicago, IL 60605

ranger rick's best

Here's a great big package from Ranger Rick! It's full of interesting, colorful articles from RANGER RICK'S NATURE MAGAZINE. The packet includes articles showing you how to make bird feeders with recycled materials and how to fight pests with pests. There's more on leaves, birdwatching, stargazing, air pollution, recycling and energy conservation. You'll even find stories about mischievous animals and how you can give first aid to hurt animals.

directions: Send a postcard.

ask for: Packet of Reprints from RANGER RICK'S MAGAZINE

write to: National Wildlife Federation
Dept. BB
1412 16th St. N.W.
Washington, D.C. 20036

send for a cricket!

CRICKET Magazine will bring you every kind of story you can imagine — and more. There are fantasies, fairy tales, exciting true adventure tales, nature and animal stories, science articles — all with beautiful illustrations. You'll find silly and serious poems, tongue twisters, jokes, puzzles and crafts you can make. You'll meet an author in each issue and Cricket and Lady Bug explain the hard words. Each month there are drawing and writing contests you can enter. CRICKET Magazine is especially for you, and you'll get a copy free!

directions: Use paper and an envelope. You must send in 50¢. (No stamps please.)

ask for: One free copy of CRICKET Magazine

write to: CRICKET Magazine
Box 100 — R.B.
La Salle, IL 61301

a book for someone special

EXPECTATIONS is a book that is printed in **BRAILLE**. It is a collection of this year's favorite stories for children. Braille pictures, some sniff pages and prize-winning poems by blind children are in it too. Do you know someone who would like to know about EXPEC-TATIONS? Perhaps you could ask the Braille Institute to send a copy to your friend. It's free to <u>any blind American child</u> in grades three through six.

directions: Use a postcard.

ask for: EXPECTATIONS

write to: Braille Institute of America, Inc.
741 N. Vermont Ave.
Los Angeles, CA 90029

prize-winning books

Pumpkins win prizes for plumpness. Books win prizes
if they are especially wonderful to read and to look at.
Pick a winner for your next book!

directions: Use paper and a long envelope. You
must enclose a stamped, self-
addressed, long envelope.

ask for: Notable Children's Booklist
Newbery Award Books List
Caldecott Award Books List

write to: Assn. for Library Service to Children
American Library Assn.
50 East Huron St.
Chicago, IL 60611

words have roots too

Did you know you can trace the roots of many
English words back to ancient times? For instance,
"neighbor" comes from two words that mean "a
nearby farmer." This booklet on word roots is from
the people who publish the Merriam-Webster Dic-
tionaries — naturally!

directions: Use a postcard.

ask for: Interesting Origins of English Words

write to: G. & C. Merriam Company
47 Federal St.
Springfield, MA 01101

rainbows everywhere

Would you like to see a world full of rainbows? You can if you get this kaleidaglas kit. Just slip the rainbow lenses into the cardboard frames that the instructions show you how to make. Then you'll see rainbows everywhere!

directions: Use paper and an envelope. You must send in 50¢.

ask for: Kaleidaglas Glasses Kit

write to: The Holex Corporation
Dept. RB
P.O. Box 27056
Philadelphia, PA 19118

more rainbows!

Now you can take rainbow pictures too. Send for this photography kit and you'll get a rainbow filter and an instruction sheet.

directions: Use paper and an envelope. You must send in $1.00.

ask for: Rainbow Photography Kit

write to: The Holex Corporation
Dept. PK
P.O. Box 27056
Philadelphia, PA 19118

would you rather be dancing?

Do you like to dance? Then you'll love the I'd Rather Be Dancing bumper sticker from CAPEZIO Ballet Makers! You'll also enjoy reading the pamphlets they have for you about toe shoes — their history, how and when to wear them. Even non-dancers will like the guide to dance exercise with photos and complete instructions.

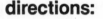

directions: Use a postcard.

ask for: I'D RATHER BE DANCING Bumper Sticker
Tips on Toe Shoes
Why Can't I Go on My Toes?
How to Achieve a Dancer's Body through Exercise

write to: CAPEZIO Ballet Makers
Dept. RB 79
1860 Broadway
New York, NY 10023

beautiful music

You can make beautiful music whenever you want with a harmonica. If you have a harmonica, you can learn how to play with the instruction booklet from the Hohner Company.

directions: Use paper and a long envelope. You must enclose a long, self-addressed, stamped envelope.

ask for: How to Play the Hohner Harmonica

write to: M. Hohner, Inc.
Andrews Road
Department MP1
Hicksville, NY 11802

blow your mind!

Did you know that harmonicas come in dozens of shapes and sizes, or that the most elaborate harmonica has over 1000 parts? Send for this large, color poster and learn all about the history of harmonicas and how they're made.

directions: Use paper and an envelope. You must send in $1.00.

ask for: Harmonica Information Poster

write to: M. Hohner, Inc.
Andrews Road
Department MP2
Hicksville, NY 11802

HOHNER HARMONICAS
The World's Best

posters of music makers

Hank Williams, Jr., and Chick Corea are musicians. Williams picks an acoustic guitar and Corea plays the electric piano. You can get a large, glossy, colorful poster of each of them!

directions: Use paper and an envelope. You must enclose $1.00 for **each** poster that you order (you don't have to get both).

ask for: Hank Williams, Jr. Guitar Poster

write to: M. Hohner, Inc.
Andrews Road
Department MP5
Hicksville, NY 11802

ask for: Chick Corea Keyboard Poster

write to: M. Hohner, Inc.
Andrews Road
Department MP4
Hicksville, NY 11802

music at christmas

Fourteen favorite Christmas carols have been collected for you in a handy little songbook. It includes the words **AND** the music so you can play along while your friends sing! Make music at Christmas!

directions: Use a postcard.

ask for: Christmas Carols

write to: John Hancock Mutual Life Ins. Co.
Community Relations T-54
Educational Material
P.O. Box 111
Boston, MA 02117

chess questions

Do you know the basics of chess? Do you want to know more about the game? Then you can send for a 21-page booklet called How Do You Play Chess? Get into the brain game — learn more about chess!

directions: Use a postcard.

ask for: How Do You Play Chess?

write to: Dover Publications, Inc.
180 Varick St.
New York, NY 10014

be a foreign coin detective

World travelers often come home with a pocketful of money from the places they visited. It's fun to see the different shapes and sizes and the strange markings. Now you can have your own pocketful of real foreign coins and paper money! You can send for five coins from the Philippines, Pakistan, Finland, Japan and India. And five paper bills from China, Japan, Korea, Hong Kong and Mexico. Can you tell where each piece comes from? Check the markings, look for clues. You can be a foreign coin detective!

directions: Use paper and an envelope. You must send in 50¢.

ask for: Free Foreign Coins and Bills

write to: Jolie Coins
Box 68
Roslyn Heights, NY 11577

stamp fun

Stan the U.S. Answer Stamp knows all about stamp collecting. Kids from all over the U.S. send him questions like, "How and why did people start using stamps?" or "How did you make the mistake of printing a stamp upside down?"

You can write your own stamp question to Stan! If your question is printed, you will get a mint set of all the U.S. commemorative stamps of 1978!

directions: Use a postcard. Write your own stamp question like this:

Dear U.S. Answer Stamp,
(Your question)
Your Name
Your Address
City, State, Zip Code

write to: U.S. Answer Stamp
Box 23501
L'Enfant Plaza Station
Washington, D.C. 20024

model rockets - a high flying hobby

Would you like to launch a real rocket? One that you made yourself? You can learn all about model rockets from The Alpha Book of Model Rocketry. Learn how to build them and how to make them soar into the air for thousands of feet. These rockets are powered by safe, inexpensive, solid fuel engines. They return gently to the ground on their own parachutes and are ready to fly again! Send for your book and catalog of rockets and you'll be on your way to an exciting, high-flying hobby.

directions: Use paper and an envelope. You must send in 50¢.

ask for: The Alpha Book of Model Rocketry
The Estes Catalogue

write to: Estes Industries
P.O. Box 227, Dept. 94
Penrose, CO 81240

model railroading

If you love model trains and you've always wanted to set up your own scale model track, here's your chance. You can send for a 32-page booklet describing everything you need to know to get started.

directions: Use a postcard.

ask for: Introduction to Scale Model Railroading

write to: Kalmbach Publishing Co.
1027 N. Seventh St.
Milwaukee, WI 53233

around the world

You'll have some great adventures when you start collecting real foreign stamps and coins. If you want to learn about the geography, history and customs of people in faraway lands, send for this packet of 50 stamps and 2 coins.

directions: Use paper and an envelope.
You must enclose 50¢.

ask for: Free Combination Selection

write to: H. E. Harris & Co., Inc.
Dept. FM-1
645 Summer St.
Boston, MA 02117

sign here, please

Did you know that collecting autographs is one of the oldest hobbies in the world? It's also very interesting and can even be profitable! Send for this foldout about an autograph club. You'll also receive a list of the addresses of 25 famous newsmakers (like President Carter), movie and TV stars (like Suzanne Somers and John Travolta), and sports heroes (like Pele). Then write away for their autographs and start your own collection!

directions: Use paper and an envelope. You must enclose a long, self-addressed, stamped envelope.

ask for: Autograph collecting information and list of addresses.

write to: UACC
P.O. Box 467, Dept. FS
Rockville Centre, NY 11571

the joy of juggling

Once you learn how to juggle you'll never forget how. And the easiest way to learn is by starting with scarves, which float lightly through the air. This illustrated booklet will teach you how to develop this challenging and entertaining skill.

directions: Use paper and an envelope. You must send in $1.00.

ask for: Juggling Scarves

write to: Juggle Bug, Inc.
23004-107th Pl. W.
Edmonds, WA 98020

juggling club

If you've really got the juggling bug maybe you'd like to think about joining a club. Send for this membership kit and you'll get a list of juggling books as well as a list of suppliers of juggling props.

directions: Use paper and an envelope. You must enclose a long, self-addressed, stamped envelope.

ask for: IJA Membership Kit

write to: International Jugglers Assn.
P.O. Box 29 - FS
Kenmore, NY 14217

fun-filled catalog

You can have a copy of the most unusual catalog in the world. It lists nearly 2000 jokes and tricks, sport and hobby items, books, electronic gadgets, camera and photo equipment, and novelties. You won't believe some of the stuff you'll find!

directions:	Use paper and an envelope. You must send in 10¢. (No stamps please.)
ask for:	The Johnson Smith Catalog
write to:	Johnson Smith Company Dept. RB 35075 Automation Dr. Mt. Clemens, MI 48043

abracadabra!

This 8-page catalog lists nifty magic tricks that amateurs and beginners can order. You'll learn to mystify your friends!

directions:	Use paper and an envelope. You must enclose a long, self-addressed, stamped envelope.
ask for:	Free Magic Catalog
write to:	Abbott's Magic Mfg. Co. 124 Joseph St. Colon, MI 49040

horse sense

Taking care of a horse is complicated. It takes time and costs money. But if you know what your horse needs, you can keep it healthy and happy. And you'll be proud to be a good horse owner! If you are thinking of buying a horse for the first time, send for this helpful 11-page booklet on horse care.

directions: Use paper and an envelope.
You must send in 55¢.

ask for: Horse Care Booklet

write to: American Humane Education
Society
Dept. HCB
350 S. Huntington Ave.
Boston, MA 02130

pet projects

If you love animals, you naturally want to help them. But before you can help them, you must know something about them. Animals and You is a 14-page booklet filled with animal activites for you and your friends to do. Just a few examples for pets: make a simple present for your pet, have a dog show or a pet show or start a dog walking service. There's a section on farm animals, zoo animals and wildlife, too. If you love animals, you'll love Animals and You!

directions: Use paper and an envelope. You must send in 65¢.

ask for: Animals and You: A Handbook of Animal Activities for People

write to: American Humane Education Society
Dept. AAY
350 S. Huntington Ave.
Boston, MA 02130

pets plus

Here's a giant coloring poster you'll want. It's 23x29 inches on heavy white paper, ready for you to color. It's filled with people and animals living happily together — in homes and apartments, in the zoo, on the farm and in the woods. We counted 140 animals in the picture!

directions: Use paper and an envelope. You must send in $1.00.

ask for: Living with Animals Coloring Poster ($1.00)

write to: American Humane Education
  Society
Dept. LACP
350 S. Huntington Ave.
Boston, MA 02130

cat care

Cats **DO** clean and housebreak themselves. But you must notice if your cat has a problem. Find out how to be a careful cat owner in the 16-page Cat Care Booklet.

directions: Use paper and an envelope. You must send in 55¢.

ask for: Cat Care Booklet

write to: American Humane Education Society
Dept. CCB
350 S. Huntington Ave.
Boston, MA 02130

small and furry

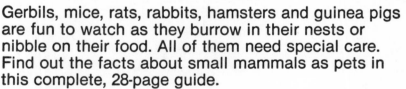

Gerbils, mice, rats, rabbits, hamsters and guinea pigs are fun to watch as they burrow in their nests or nibble on their food. All of them need special care. Find out the facts about small mammals as pets in this complete, 28-page guide.

directions: Use paper and an envelope. You must send in 55¢.

ask for: Small Mammal Care

write to: American Humane Education Society
Dept. SMC
350 S. Huntington Ave.
Boston, MA 02130

animal first aid

You probably know a few things you should do as first aid for people. But do you know what to do if your pet gets hurt suddenly and you need to give it first aid? There's a first aid guide for animals just for you! It was written by veterinarians to teach you how to care for your pet in an emergency. Send for it, read it, and be prepared!

directions: Use paper and an envelope. You must send in 65¢.

ask for: The Angell Memorial Guide to Animal First Aid

write to: American Humane Education Society
Dept. AMG
350 S. Huntington Ave.
Boston, MA 02130

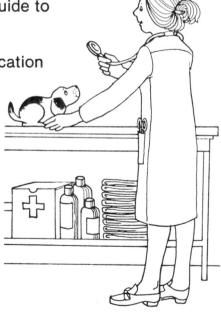

feathered friends

Birds make good pets. They are friendly and talkative. They can even do tricks. Birds are easy to care for because they don't need to go for walks or get brushed. But birds must have food and water every day. And they need attention and someone to talk to! Be the best bird owner you can be. Read the 12-page booklet on Bird Care.

directions: Use paper and an envelope. You must send in 55¢.

ask for: Bird Care Booklet

write to: American Humane Education Society
Dept. BCB
350 S. Huntington Ave.
Boston, MA 02130

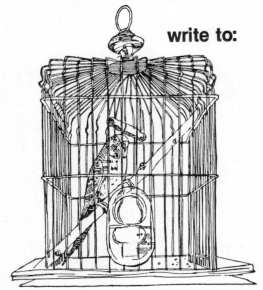

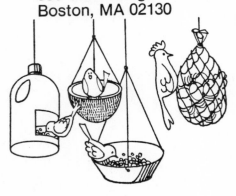

bow-wow!

There are over 100 dog breeds today. And hundreds of mixed breeds! Before you choose a dog of your own, ask yourself the questions in this helpful guide to dog care. The 20-page booklet includes many tips for feeding, grooming and training your dog.

directions: Use paper and an envelope. You must send in 55¢.

ask for: Dog Care Booklet

write to: American Humane Education Society
Dept. DCB
350 S. Huntington Ave.
Boston, MA 02130

a well-trained dog

Your dog wants to be a happy member of your family. He deserves to be well-trained so that he won't be scolded! A well-trained dog should learn six simple rules. You can find out how to teach him these rules by sending for the 28-page dog care booklet from Ken-L Ration.

directions: Use a postcard.

ask for: How to Care for, Train and Feed Your Dog

write to: Ken-L Ration Dog Care Booklet
Box 6333
Chicago, IL 60677

the quarter horse

With rippling muscles and shining coat, she whinnies and neighs for you to hurry. You jump on her back and you're off and flying down the track! What fun to imagine yourself winning a race on a champion quarter horse. Now you can send for booklets that will tell you about the care and training of quarter horses.

directions: Use a postcard.

ask for: Packet of booklets about quarter horses

write to: The American Quarter Horse
  Association
Dept. R.B.3
Amarillo, TX 79168

You can also get a chart and a full-color poster of a quarter horse.

directions: Use a postcard

ask for: Poster and chart

write to: The American Quarter Horse
  Association
Dept. R.B.3
Amarillo, TX 79168

animal health

TODAY'S ANIMAL HEALTH is a magazine for people who are interested in the health and welfare of animals. Send for your own sample copy.

directions: Use paper and an envelope. You must send in $1.00.

ask for: Sample copy of TODAY'S ANIMAL HEALTH

write to: TODAY'S ANIMAL HEALTH
8338 Rosemead Blvd.
Pico Rivera, CA 90660

fisherman's friend

Bet you don't have a bumper sticker that reads "Preserve Portuguese Water Dogs"! Bet you don't even know what a Portuguese Water Dog looks like! Send away for a bumper sticker and information about this remarkable dog that catches fish and dives for objects lost underwater.

directions: Use paper and a long envelope. You must enclose a long, stamped, self-addressed envelope and 50¢.

ask for: Preserving Portuguese Waterdogs

write to: Mrs. Herbert H. Miller, Jr.
One Greenley Road
New Canaan, CT 06840

pet packet

The purpose of the American Society for the Prevention of Cruelty to Animals is to encourage people to treat animals humanely. Send for a whole packet of stuff about animals, including bookmarks, an 8-page coloring book, and three information sheets about dogs.

directions:	Use paper and an envelope. You must send in 50¢.
ask for:	Animal Care — Free Stuff
write to:	Animal Care — Free Stuff ASPCA, Education Dept. 441 East 92nd St. New York, NY 10028

kids' best friends

Your cat and dog are sometimes your best friends, right? Learn how to treat them better by sending away for these two booklets that have pictures you can color.

directions:	Use paper and an envelope. You must enclose 20¢ for each booklet that you order.
ask for:	Kittens and Cats You and Your Dog
write to:	Animal Welfare Institute P.O. Box 3650 Washington, D.C. 20007

MEADOWBROOK
PRESS

FREE STUFF
FOR KIDS

49

make your own pinhole camera ✗

Learn why cameras work! This 12-page booklet shows exactly how to make your own pinhole camera from a tin can or box or old film cartridge. It takes real pictures!

directions: Use paper and a long envelope. You must enclose a long, self-addressed envelope.
Do not put a stamp on that envelope, but put the title and number of the booklet on the **BACK** of it.

ask for: How to Make and Use a Pinhole Camera (AA-5)

write to: Photo Information Dept. 841
Eastman Kodak Co.
343 State St.
Rochester, NY 14650

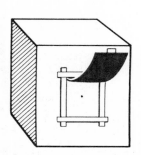

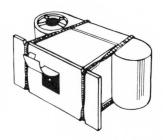

the largest living things

Do you know what they are? The redwood trees of California! Some are 3200 years old! Learn more about the giants of America!

directions: Use paper and an envelope. You must send in 50¢.

ask for: 4 Pamphlets about Redwoods

write to: Service Library, Dept. ORH
California Redwood Assn.
One Lombard St.
San Francisco, CA 94111

making water go uphill

Who says you can't make water go uphill? You can make water pumps that really work! Each folder has clear instructions and drawings.

directions: Use paper and an envelope. You must send in 50¢ for each folder. You must also enclose a long, self-addressed, stamped envelope.

ask for: A Balloon and Funnel Pump
A Tin Can Pump

write to: The Museum's Shop
The Children's Museum
300 Congress St.
Boston, MA 02110

exploring science

Are you a budding young scientist? Do you want to learn more about how science works? Send for this 35-page catalog. It's packed with items like tubes and beakers, magnets and minerals, books and science kits. You'll also get a free mineral sample!

directions: Use a postcard.

ask for: Science Catalog and Mineral

write to: Schubel & Son
Educational Science Kits
P.O. Box 214848
Sacramento, CA 95821

prospector's paradise

Do you know what amethyst looks like? Have you ever seen a shark's tooth? Send for any of these samples and start your own collection. Each sample is about 1 inch in size and comes in a small clear plastic bag labeled with the name of the sample and the place where it's found. You can choose from this list:

Amethyst	Opal
Dinosaur Bone	Petrified Wood
Gold Ore	Soapstone
Marble	Turquoise
Mica	Shark's Tooth

directions: Use paper and an envelope. You must send in 70¢ for **each** sample that you request.

ask for: Each sample that you want by name.

write to: Schubel & Son
Educational Science Kits
P.O. Box 214848
Sacramento, CA 95821

cactus eggs?

You may live in a state where cacti don't grow, but did you know that you can grow your very own cactus at home? Send for this Cactus Egg. It's 3½ inches high and made of clear plastic. In it you'll find a seed capsule with 50 seeds and a small bag of soil mix. An instruction sheet shows you how to get your cacti going in the egg itself — a miniature terrarium!

directions: Use paper and an envelope. You must send in $1.00.

ask for: Cactus Egg

write to: K & L Cactus Nursery
Dept. "Rainbow Egg"
12712 Stockton Blvd.
Galt, CA 95632

sun power

Are you curious about how to get power from the sun? Write for a booklist and get six 3x9-inch cards with descriptions and diagrams of ways to heat with solar energy.

directions: Use a postcard.

ask for: Solar Energy Booklist for Children and Teenagers
Six Information Cards about Solar Heating

write to: National Solar Heating & Cooling Information Center
P.O. Box 1607
Rockville, MD 20850

seed power

The sun's power also helps vegetables grow from seed. Send for a large packet of seeds, plant them and watch a 20-foot row of your favorite vegetables grow.

directions: Use paper and an envelope. You must send in 25¢.

ask for: Packet of seeds of whatever vegetable you wish to grow.

write to: Butterbrooke Farm
78-K Barry Road
Oxford, CT 06483

earth forces ✕

Did you know that there are more than 500 active volcanoes in the world today? Or that most earthquakes occur in areas bordering the Pacific Ocean? Or that some geysers erupt every minute while others remain quiet for months? Find out more about these fascinating earth forces by sending away for these pamphlets and foldouts. You'll learn all about their interesting causes and their sometimes destructive effects.

directions: Use a postcard.

ask for:
Volcanoes
Earthquakes
Geysers

write to:
U.S. Geological Survey
Branch of Distribution
1200 S. Eads St.
Arlington, VA 22202

high in the sky

Let's see. Cumulus clouds are the big billowy ones and cirrus clouds are thin and wispy. Or is it the other way around? Send for this colorful 11x17-inch chart and learn all about clouds. Over thirty different photographs will help you identify the clouds you see outdoors. And captions underneath the photos will tell you all about what kind of weather to expect when you see that kind of cloud.

directions: Use paper and an envelope. You must send in $1.00.

ask for: Cloud Chart

write to: Cloud Chart
Attn: Robby
P.O. Box 1122
Glen Allen, VA 23060

a drop in the bucket

Do you know how much rain fell last time it rained? You don't need expensive equipment to be able to tell and you don't need to be a TV weatherman, either. Send for this simple, effective rain gauge and be the weatherman around your house! The glass vial, which measures the rain in both inches and millimeters, fits into a metal bracket. You screw the bracket into any flat area that's out in the open — like a fence post. Then sit back and wait for it to rain!

directions: Use paper and an envelope. You must send in $1.00.

ask for: Rain Gauge No. 810

write to: Childrens/Rewards
Box 1776
West Bend, WI 53095

right in your own back yard

What can you do when there's nothing to do? Send for this packet of interesting brochures and booklets and you'll learn about the world of things to do in your own back yard. You'll find out how to start a bird calendar in the spring, how to get a garden going in the summer, and how to make a picture record of where the sun sets on the horizon all during the year. There's lots more you can do without leaving your neighborhood!

directions: Use paper and an envelope. You must enclose a long, self-addressed envelope that has 28¢ worth of stamps on it.

ask for: Doing Is Fun
How to Grow a Garden
What Do You Mean—Birdlike
  Appetites?

write to: Conservation Committee
The Garden Club of America
598 Madison Avenue
New York, NY 10022

energy news

What is energy and why do people say there is an energy crisis? We now get energy to run our cars and heat our homes from fuels like gasoline and coal. But the earth is running out of those fuels, so people are trying to find new sources of energy. Learn more in Earthbeats Newspaper.

directions: Send a postcard.

ask for: Earthbeats Newspaper No. 1 on Energy

write to: Sea Grant College Program
University of Wisconsin
1800 University Ave.
Madison, WI 53706

building safe campfires

Protect the forests and the animals that live there — learn to build and put out your campfires safely. Send for this handy foldout from Smokey the Bear.

directions: Use a postcard.

ask for: Make Campfires Safe!

write to: Forest Service, U.S.D.A.
P.O. Box 2417
Washington, D.C. 20013

spaceship earth ×

Earth is a spaceship traveling around the sun. It needs fuel and every person on it needs food. Send for Mr. Peanut's 22-page booklet on ecology to find out how to help take care of our spaceship earth.

directions: Use a postcard.

ask for: Mr. Peanut's Guide to Ecology

write to: Standard Brands Educational
    Service
Box 2695
Grand Central Station
New York, NY 10017

inland seas

The Great Lakes are the largest bodies of fresh water in the world. You'll learn lots of facts about them in this booklet and newspaper on the Great Lakes.

directions: Use a postcard.

ask for: Our Great Lakes Booklet
Earthbeats No. 2 — Great Lakes

write to: Sea Grant College Program
University of Wisconsin
1800 University Ave.
Madison, WI 53706

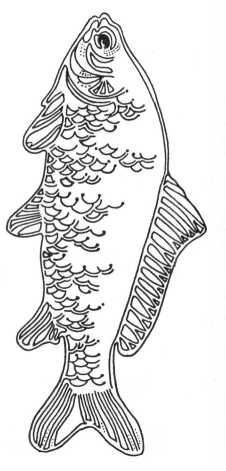

friends of animals

Have you heard the story of Elsa the lioness or seen the movie BORN FREE? The Elsa Clubs of America, founded by the author of BORN FREE, are devoted to educating people about the endangered wildlife of the world. Send for a colorful bumper sticker or badge (or both) and you'll also receive some interesting information about these clubs and their projects.

directions: Use paper and an envelope. You must enclose 75¢ for **each** item that you request.

ask for: Born Free Bumper Sticker (75¢)
Born Free Badge (75¢)

write to: Elsa Wild Animal Appeal
P.O. Box 4572-X
North Hollywood, CA 91607

for the birds!

Do you know how to invite birds to your home? You plant the trees and bushes that give them the best shelter and food! The U.S. Soil Conservation Service has booklets which tell you what plants and foods make perfect homes for the feathered friends in your area. Color photos give you a good idea of what each bird and each best-for-bird plant looks like.

directions: Use a postcard.

ask for: Invite Birds to Your Home
(Say which area you live in —
midwest, northwest, northeast or
    southeast)

write to: Soil Conservation Service
U.S.D.A.
P.O. Box 2890
Washington, D.C. 20013

You can also write to your local Soil Conservation Service Office. It is listed in your telephone book under United States Government, Department of Agriculture.

crafty critters from plastic containers

Learn to recycle and make fun things at the same time in this folder from TEXIZE. Use empty trigger sprayers and refill bottles to make bird houses, mooseheads, and even a Fourth-of-July eagle! The simple instructions show you how to make a whole zoo full of Crafty Critters.

directions: Use a postcard.

ask for: Crafty Critters Folder

write to: Consumer Relations Dept.
Box MP
TEXIZE
P.O. Box 368
Greenville, SC 29602

michael recycle to the rescue

You can help Michael Recycle rescue the world's natural resources by recycling. Instead of throwing away a soda pop can or a TV dinner tray, you can recycle them by selling the aluminum back to the Reynolds Company. Michael will tell you all about his recycling rescue mission in a colorful comic book.

directions: Use a postcard.

ask for: Reynolds Aluminum Presents
  Michael Recycle

write to: Recycling Public Relations Manager
Reynolds Metals Co.
Box 27003
Richmond, VA 23261

woodsy owl and the great outdoors

Do you go camping in the woods? Do you like to hike in the great outdoors? If you do, here's important information you should have. You get an 8½x11 inch full-color Woodsy Owl poster with tips on improving the environment. You also get Woodsy Owl's tips on camping. By learning good outdoor habits, you can protect the environment for everyone. As Woodsy Owl says, "Give a hoot! Don't pollute!"

directions: Use a postcard.

ask for: Woodsy Owl Poster
Tips on Camping

write to: Woodsy Owl
Forest Service, U.S.D.A.
P.O. Box 1963
Washington, D.C. 20013

the story of paper

Think about all you'd have to do without if paper had never been invented. This book! The funny papers! Baseball cards! Send for a large 32x22-inch poster from the American Paper Institute. It traces paper's fascinating history from its origins in China nearly 2000 years ago, through its development in Europe, and finally to its production in America a few hundred years ago.

directions: Use a postcard.

ask for: How Paper Came to America

write to: Wall Chart
American Paper Institute
260 Madison Ave.
New York, NY 10016

how the telephone works

Have you ever wondered how you can send the sound of your voice across town or across the country — just by picking up the telephone? Have you tried to imagine what it would take to invent the telephone? You'll find answers to these questions in two fascinating booklets about the telephone and its inventor Alexander Graham Bell. They're available from your local phone company.

directions: To get these booklets, you give the phone company a call! When you call:
1. Speak clearly and not too fast.
2. Expect to wait until you are connected with the person who can help you. Be patient and hang on!
3. Explain what you want. Give your name and address very carefully.

ask for: The How the Telephone Works Booklet
The Alexander Graham Bell Booklet

call: The Business Office of your local phone company. (If you don't know the name of the phone company in your area, ask your parents or teacher. Then look up the number in your telephone book.)

what's watt

How is electricity made? Why is the cost of electricity going up? What new sources of power can help us make electricity? For hundreds of facts about electricity, send for your complete, 36-page booklet.

directions: Use a postcard.

ask for: You and Your Electric Company Booklet

write to: Educational Services
Edison Electric Institute
1111 19th St., N.W.
Washington, D.C. 20036

fishing facts

Like to fish? These two 36-page booklets will give you all the facts about the fish in Lake Michigan and Lake Superior, with lots of drawings to help you identify each kind. You'll learn about more than 20 kinds of fish including the sea lamprey.

directions: Use a postcard.

ask for: Fish of Lake Superior
Fish of Lake Michigan

write to: Sea Grant College Program
University of Wisconsin
1800 University Ave.
Madison, WI 53706

find the blimp!

Have you ever seen a photograph of the Goodrich Blimp? You'll have to order the color postcard to see what the surprise is! You can also get a big 22x34 inch wall chart about tires. You'll see in detailed drawings all the things that go into the making of a modern tire.

directions: Use a postcard.

ask for: Goodrich Blimp Postcard
The Inside Story of Today's Tires
 Chart

write to: Community Relations
The B.F. Goodrich Co.
500 S. Main St.
Akron, OH 44318

the adventures of steel

Iron ore, limestone and coke are the raw ingredients of steel. All three are dug out of the ground. People worry about the big empty holes that are left behind. What is the steel industry doing about them? You can find out by sending for two large colorful fold-outs.

directions: Use a postcard.

ask for: Story of Environment and Industry
Story of Steel

write to: U.S. Steel Corp.
Room 727
Educational Services
600 Grant St.
Pittsburgh, PA 15230

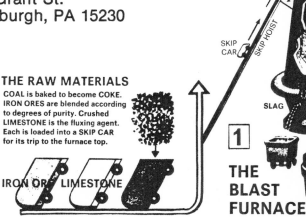

THE RAW MATERIALS

COAL is baked to become COKE. IRON ORES are blended according to degrees of purity. Crushed LIMESTONE is the fluxing agent. Each is loaded into a SKIP CAR for its trip to the furnace top.

IRON ORE   LIMESTONE

SKIP CAR   SKIP HOIST

STOVE

HOT GASES

HOT AIR

COLD AIR

SLAG

MOLTEN IRON
2500°F

1

THE BLAST FURNACE

making paper by machine

What does it take to turn a tree into a piece of paper? This folder from Hammermill shows you how paper is made in giant paper factories. Photos show each step.

directions: Use a postcard.

ask for: From Forest Tree to Fine Papers

write to: Educational Services
Hammermill Papers Group
East Lake Rd.
Erie, PA 16533

making paper by hand

You can make paper by hand with the papermaking kit from Hammermill. The instruction booklet tells you exactly how to do it.

directions: Use paper and an envelope.
You must send in 25¢ for postage and handling.

ask for: How to Make Paper by Hand

write to: Educational Services
Hammermill Papers Group
East Lake Rd.
Erie, PA 16533

the story of oil

Did you know that if we had no liquid petroleum, three-fourths of our energy and almost 3,000 oil products would disappear? Our country needs oil to drive trucks, cars, trains and planes. Oil also heats buildings. And it helps to make paints, plastics, fabrics, fertilizers and much more! Union Oil Company is in the business of finding oil, bringing it out of the ground, refining it and then bringing it to the people who use it. Find out about The Story of Oil. Send for the huge 25x38 inch color fold-out. There's a fold-out on The Story of Geothermal Energy too.

directions: Use a postcard.

ask for: The Story of Oil
The Story of Geothermal Energy

write to: Corporate Communications
Union Oil Co.
Dept. MP
Box 7600
Los Angeles, CA 90051

metres are neater!

You'll agree when you send for the Marvelous Metrics Package from The Math Group. You get a brightly colored Metric Marvels Poster with funny drawings of how things really measure up in metrics. Things like the fastest animal, the smallest coin, the worst snowfall, the biggest pizza. The poster measures 52x70 centimetres! You'll also get your own Metric Ruler and a Metric Measuring Puzzle for practicing with your ruler. When you finish the puzzle, you can show it to your teacher and ask her/him to sign your Order of the Neater Metre Diploma. Then you can proudly wear your real metal Think Metric Pin!

directions: Use paper and an envelope.
You must send in $1.00.

ask for: The Marvelous Metrics Package

write to: The Math Group, Inc.
Metric Package
396 E. 79th St.
Minneapolis, MN 55420

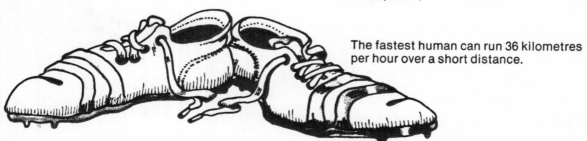

The fastest human can run 36 kilometres per hour over a short distance.

world-wide metrics ✗

In 1790, scientists in France invented the metric system. Today most countries in the world use the metric system for measuring. Only the United States and a few small countries don't. In 1975 the United States decided it was time to change to the metric system. A national program was started to help people learn about metrics. Now you can send for your own metric information packet.

directions: Use a postcard.

ask for: Metric Information for Students

write to: Metric Information
U.S. Metric Board
1815 N. Lynn St.
Suite 600
Arlington, VA 22209

25 DEGREES CELSIUS

25 DEGREES FAHRENHEIT

fund raising

Raise money for your school, team club or charity by selling FREE STUFF FOR KIDS. Our fund-raising brochure explains how to go about selling books at your fund-raising event, and it shows you how much money you can make doing it!

directions: Use paper and an envelope. You must enclose a long, self-addressed, stamped envelope.

ask for: Fund Raising Information

write to: Meadowbrook Press
Dept. FR
16648 Meadowbrook Lane
Wayzata, MN 55391

MEADOWBROOK PRESS

FREE STUFF
FOR KIDS

77

TAKING
CARE

fireside fun

Have some family fun around the fireside! Even if you don't have a fireplace you'll enjoy the Fireside Kit from Duraflame. The kit contains a large poster that you can color, a fire safety game called MASTER SWEEP, and a 12-page booklet that's full of fun and facts.

directions: Use paper and an envelope. You must send in $1.00.

ask for: Fireside Kit

write to: Fireside Kit
P.O. Box 24305
Oakland, CA 94623

be a better biker ✗

The Schwinn Bicycle Company will send you a packet of four colorful folders to help keep your bike in better shape. Learn 12 important rules of the road, the **RIGHT** ways to lock your bicycle, how to keep out of tire trouble and how to care for a 5 or 10 speed bike.

directions: Use a postcard.

ask for: Bicycle Safety
Lock Your Bike
Tire Care Guide
Care & Operation Checklist

write to: Consumer Relations Dept.
Schwinn Bicycle Co.
1856 N. Kostner Ave.
Chicago, IL 60639

bike safety ✗

Send for the Bicycle Blue Book — it tells the hand signals to use for turning and stopping and how to care for your bike to keep it safe.

directions: Use a postcard.

ask for: Bicycle Blue Book

write to: Public Relations Dept.
The Goodyear Tire & Rubber Co.
Akron, OH 44316

✗ lumps for "bumps"

Poor little "Bumps" is always hurting himself in one way or another. No wonder he's always frowning — he has to wear his arm in a sling. Send for this coloring book full of games and puzzles. With it you'll learn how to be more careful around the house. And you'll also have a lot of fun!

directions: Use paper and an envelope. You must enclose 50¢.

ask for: It Hurts When They Cry— "Bumps" Activity Book (052-003-00177-2)

write to: Superintendent of Documents
U.S. Gov. Printing Office
Washington, D.C. 20402

leon the careless lizard

Leon is a bright green lizard, but sometimes he is not very bright where it counts...in his head! He is always running into things, falling down and getting hurt in one way or another. Read the adventures of Leon and find out how **NOT** to get hurt. The big 24-page booklet is fun to read and you can color the pictures if you have enough green crayons.

directions: Use paper and an envelope. You must send in 60¢.

ask for: Little Leon the Lizard

write to: Consumer Information Center
Dept. 112H
Pueblo, CO 81009

help sparky prevent fires

Help Sparky, the fire safety dog, prevent fires! Just send for his Fire Department Membership Kit. You'll get an official identification card, a badge, a pledge card and your own Official Fire Inspector's Handbook.

directions: Use paper and an envelope. You must send in 50¢.

ask for: Sparky's Fire Department Membership Kit

write to: Public Affairs Dept.
National Fire Protection Assn.
470 Atlantic Ave.
Boston, MA 02210

Sparky's fire department has a handy checklist for you. It helps you find important fire danger in your house.

directions: Use paper and a long envelope. You must enclose a long, self-addressed, stamped envelope.

ask for: Sparky's Checklist

write to: Public Affairs
National Fire Protection Assn.
470 Atlantic Ave.
Boston, MA 02210

water ways

Do you know the "rules of the road" when you're in a boat? This 4x6-inch red and black decal explains how boats should pass each other and what various whistle signals mean. It also tells you about storm warning flags and channel buoy guides. Stick it on your family's boat or decorate your bulletin board with it.

directions: Use paper and an envelope. You must enclose a long, self-addressed, stamped envelope.

ask for: Common Sense Afloat

write to: National Marine Manufacturers
Association
Public Relations Dept.
401 North Michigan Ave.
Chicago, IL 60611

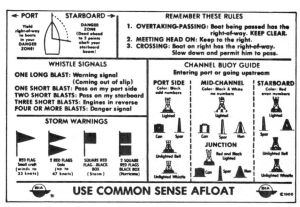

tornado!

Owlie Skywarn will tell you what to do if you know a tornado is coming — at home, at school or on the street. He wants you to learn the tornado danger signs — bad thunderstorms, hail, a loud roar, a dark funnel-shaped cloud. His 16-page booklet has pictures, projects and a crossword puzzle too.

directions: Use a postcard.

ask for: Tornado Warning (PA75012)

write to: Central Logistics Supply Center
619 Hardesty St.
Kansas City, MO 64124

hurricane!

In a hurricane, the wind blows as much as 200 miles per hour! Rain comes down in solid sheets. Buildings are blown apart and people are hurt or even killed. Find out what you can do to be safe in a hurricane in this 16-page booklet from Owlie Skywarn.

directions: Use a postcard.

ask for: Hurricane Warning (PA 77001)

write to: Central Logistics Supply Center
619 Hardesty St.
Kansas City, MO 64124

lightning! ✗

Did you know that lightning kills more people than tornadoes and hurricanes together? Every day lightning strikes somewhere in the world. Lightning is dangerous, but you don't have to be afraid of it if you know how to protect yourself. Owlie Skywarn will teach you what lightning is. And he'll show you how you can stay away from it! Order his 16-page booklet for boys and girls.

directions: Use a postcard.

ask for: Owlie Skywarn's Lightning Book
       (PA 77023)

write to: Central Logistics Supply Center
       619 Hardesty St.
       Kansas City, MO 64124

primitive pete's tool chest

Primitive Pete lived so long ago there was no one around to show him how to use tools. Send for the ABC's of Hand Tools and let Pete show you the right and wrong ways to use and care for all your hand tools. You'll find many helpful hints in this 47-page booklet.

directions: Use a postcard.

ask for: The ABC's of Hand Tools

write to: Public Relations Staff — Booklets
General Motors Corp.
General Motors Bldg.
Detroit, MI 48202

grow a pineapple!

We all know that pineapples grow in Hawaii. But did you know that you can grow one in your own home — wherever you live? You use the leafy top (called the crown) of a pineapple that you already have. Send for these two foldouts. One shows you how to start your own plant and tend it while it's growing. The other lists 12 pineapple recipes — you can read them while you're waiting for yours to grow!

directions: Use a postcard.

ask for: How You Can Grow a Pineapple in Your Own Home
For Kids of All Ages Who Cook

write to: Castle & Cooke Foods
Dept. PK
50 California St.
San Francisco, CA 94111

delicious! nutritious!

Want to know what basic nutrition is all about — the easy way? California apricot growers have developed a handy cardboard nutrition calculator to help you understand the importance of essential nutrients to good health. You can also get a colorful foldout that shows you how to make various snacks with delicious and nutritious apricots.

directions: Use a postcard.

ask for: Nutrition Calculator
Snacks, Munchies, Nibbles and
     Mini-Meals

write to: California Apricot Advisory Board
1295 Boulevard Way
Walnut Creek, CA 94595

breakfast basics

What's **your** breakfast score? Have fun and learn about nutrition by using this foldout to keep a daily record of what you eat for breakfast over a 4-week period.

directions: Use a postcard.

ask for: Breakfast Scorecard

write to: Kellogg Company
Dept. FSK
Battle Creek, MI 49016

food facts

Are you writing a report on nutrition? These five folders might be just the thing you need. Find out what you need to know to take good care of yourself!

directions: Use paper and an envelope.
You must send in $1.00.

ask for: The Midget Encyclopedia

write to: Midget Encyclopedia
P.O. Box 7226F
Washington, D.C. 20044

hot dog!

Americans eat 14 billion hot dogs every year. That's 500 eaten every second of every day of every year! This cartoon pamphlet outlines the history of hot dogs and some facts about them.

directions: Use a postcard.

ask for: Hooray for the Hot Dog!

write to: Oscar Mayer & Co.
Consumer Affairs FSFK
P.O. Box 7188
Madison, WI 53707

everything you knead

Kneading is a way to punch dough to make bread turn out nice and fluffy. Learn to knead and bake bread and buns by sending for two colorful booklets from Fleishmann's.

directions: Use a postcard.

ask for: The Young Cook's Bake-A-Bread
 Book
The Young Cook's Bake-A-Bun Book

write to: Fleishmann's Yeast
Box 509
Madison Square Station
New York, NY 10010

have a ball with popcorn!

Everybody loves popcorn the good, old-fashioned way with lots of salt and melted butter. You can send for a free folder with dozens of ideas for other terrific popcorn treats. Yum!

directions: Use a postcard.

ask for: 15 Jolly Time Recipes for Pop Corn Lovers

write to: Jolly Time Pop Corn
American Pop Corn Co.
Box 178
Sioux City, IA 51102

no sticky fingers

You can make a perfect popcorn ball without burning your fingers or getting them all sticky. Send for this bright red plastic popcorn ball maker. You'll also get two recipes.

directions: Use paper and an envelope. You must send in $1.00.

ask for: Jolly Time Pop Corn Ball Maker

write to: Jolly Time Pop Corn
American Pop Corn Co.
Box 178
Sioux City, IA 51102

take a deep breath

Your lungs help you breathe best when they're clean. You can get information about how your lungs work plus puzzles and leaflets that explain how dirty air harms your lungs from the American Lung Association.

directions: Use a postcard.

ask for: Information about how lungs work
Air pollution information
Puzzles about smoking and air pollution

write to: American Lung Assn. - RB
G.P.O. 596
New York, NY 10001

i'll never smoke

The Lung Association has information about smoking plus buttons, signs and posters.

directions: Use a postcard.

ask for: Information about smoking
Buttons about smoking
Signs about smoking
Posters about smoking

write to: American Lung Assn. - RB
G.P.O. 596
New York, NY 10001

look inside your eye ✕

Have you ever wondered what it's like **INSIDE** your eye? You can send for a color drawing of how your eye looks inside your head. It will show you all the different parts that go together to make it possible for you to see!

directions: Use paper and a long envelope. You must enclose a long, self-addressed, stamped envelope.

ask for: Schematic Section of the Human Eye

write to: Communications Division
American Optometric Assn.
243 N. Lindbergh
St. Louis, MO 63141

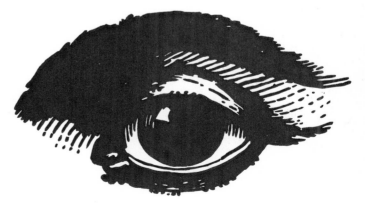

how blind people read

Blind people do not read as you do. They enjoy stories by reading with their finger tips! By feeling raised dots on heavy paper, they can read the braille alphabet. You can order a sheet with the braille alphabet on it. You'll see how the dots go together to make letters and words.

directions: Use paper and a long envelope. You must enclose a long self-addressed, stamped envelope.

ask for: Braille Alphabet Sheet

write to: Communication Center
State Services for the Blind
1745 University Ave.
St. Paul, MN 55104

a	b	c	d	e	f	g	h	i	j

k	l	m	n	o	p	q	r	s	t

u	v	w	x	y	z

native americans

If your teacher asked you to write a report on Native Americans, would you know how to start? The Bureau of Indian Affairs has information on famous individuals and tribes, their wars, their music and food, their languages and religions.

directions: Use a postcard.

ask for: Information about Native Americans. (Tell them the topics you are most interested in.)

write to: Bureau of Indian Affairs
Office of Public Information
1951 Constitution Ave. N.W.
Washington, D.C. 20245

food and shelter

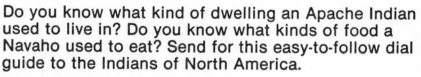

Do you know what kind of dwelling an Apache Indian used to live in? Do you know what kinds of food a Navaho used to eat? Send for this easy-to-follow dial guide to the Indians of North America.

directions: Use paper and an envelope. You must send in 25¢.

ask for: Guide to Indians of North America

write to: Indian Guide
Lowrey's
P.O. Box 9128
Denver, CO 80209

notable women

How much do you know about the outstanding women in America's history? Maybe not as much as you'd like to! Now you can send for a 28-page question and answer booklet. You'll learn about women who have achieved something important for themselves and for their country. You'll get to know over 70 women from the past and the present — writers and scientists, aviators and athletes, politicians and professors.

directions: Use a postcard.

ask for: Women in America

write to: The Sperry and Hutchinson Co.
Consumer Services
2900 W. Seminary Dr.
Fort Worth, TX 76133

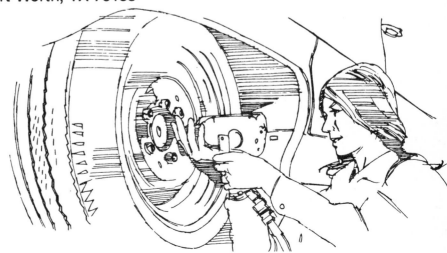

history comes alive

It's more fun to study history when you can look at and touch a piece of it. What did the Declaration of Independence actually look like? How about the Bill of Rights? Or a poster offering a $25,000 reward for Jesse James — Dead or Alive? Send for these antiqued parchment replicas of actual historical documents, posters, banknotes and maps. Each piece of parchment goes through a secret 11-step process that makes it really look and feel old!

directions: Use paper and an envelope. You may order as many different items or sets of items as you wish. You must send in the appropriate amount of money listed after the name of **each** item you order from the next page.

ask for: Each item (or packet of items) by its name **and** number.

write to: Historical Documents Co.
Dept. K
8 North Preston St.
Philadelphia, PA 19104

Here is a list of historical posters, documents, maps and banknotes to choose from.

#J506K: Jesse James poster and free replica of an 1840 U.S. banknote....send 50¢.

#B506K: Billy the Kid poster and free replica of an 1840 U.S. banknote....send 50¢.

#L509K: The Many Faces of Lincoln poster and free replica of an 1840 U.S. banknote ....send 50¢.

#101K: Declaration of Independence, Bill of Rights, History of American Flags.... send $1.00 for the set.

#104K: Map of the Voyages of Discovery, map of the Revolutionary War, map of the Civil War....send $1.00 for the set.

#102K: 14 different Colonial and Revolutionary banknotes....send $1.00 for the set.

#111K: 1 Continental coin and 1 Continental banknote....send $1.00 for the set.

#103K: 12 different Confederate banknotes... send $1.00 for the set.

stars and stripes

"The Star Spangled Banner," "Old Glory," "The Stars and Stripes" — these are all names for the American flag. But did you know there have been 27 versions of our flag? And did you know that Betsy Ross probably didn't really design the first one? You can find out all sorts of interesting facts about our flag by sending for folders from the Veterans of Foreign Wars.

directions: Use paper and a long envelope. You must enclose a long, self-addressed, stamped envelope.

ask for: Etiquette on the Stars and Stripes
Ten Short Flag Stories
Questions and Answers on the U.S. Flag

write to: Americanism Director
V.F.W.
406 W. 34th St.
Kansas City, MO 64111

The Fifth Flag (1820)

The Sixth Flag (1822)

The Seventh Flag (1836)

crazy car stickers

You can get a packet of automobile stickers just like the ones real racing drivers have on their cars! Bright colors! Famous brand names! They're the real thing!

directions: Use paper and an envelope. You must send in $1.00.

ask for: Packet of Crown/Auto Automotive Stickers

write to: Crown/Auto, Inc.
P.O. Box 1217
Minneapolis, MN 55440

versatile vehicles

Snowplows and tractors, moving vans and cement mixers, bookmobiles and log haulers — all of them are TRUCKS. Find out the history of trucks and how they work for you in this big, 56-page booklet. Photos on every page show more kinds of trucks than you can imagine!

directions: Use a postcard.

ask for: Lifelines: How Trucks Serve America

write to: Motor Vehicle Manufacturers Assn.
300 New Center Bldg.
Detroit, MI 48202

keep on truckin'

Do you want to know more about the trucker's world? Here's a big colorful wall chart with photos of 30 different trucks and buses and descriptions of the work they do.

directions: Use a postcard.

ask for: Trucks and Buses Serve America

write to: Motor Vehicle Manufacturing Assn.
300 New Center Bldg.
Detroit, MI 48202

cb for truckers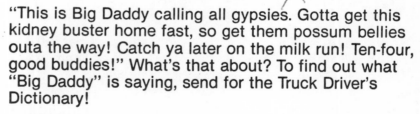

"This is Big Daddy calling all gypsies. Gotta get this kidney buster home fast, so get them possum bellies outa the way! Catch ya later on the milk run! Ten-four, good buddies!" What's that about? To find out what "Big Daddy" is saying, send for the Truck Driver's Dictionary!

directions: Use a postcard.

ask for: Truck Driver's Dictionary

write to: Educational Services. RB
American Trucking Assn., Inc.
1616 P St. N.W.
Washington, D.C. 20036

a traveling treasure hunt

Are you hunting for some new car games? You can send for Travel Games, a 31-page booklet filled with game ideas for family fun. It has directions (and scoring space) for dozens of games that everyone can play — highway contests, nature word hunts, games with signs, license plates, fences, roofs, colors and sounds. Each one is a traveling treasure hunt!

directions: Use paper and an envelope. You must send in 75¢.

ask for: Travel Games

write to: The Beavers
Star Route, Box 184
Laporte, MN 56461

exploring the appalachian trail

Imagine yourself as a young pioneer. You set out in Maine and end up in Georgia, following the longest footpath in the world — the Appalachian Trail! Send for a pamphlet describing the trail and guides to it.

directions: Use a postcard.

ask for: The Appalachian Trail

write to: Appalachian Trail Conference
Box 236
Harper's Ferry, WV 25425

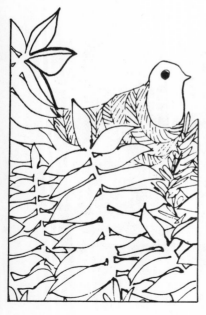

america's national parks

Special areas are chosen to be National Parks because they are beautiful, or are important in history, or have an unusual natural feature — like Old Faithful, the geyser in Yellowstone National Park. Send for a full-color guide to all the National Parks!

directions: Use paper and an evelope. You must enclose 70¢.

ask for: Guide to National Parks

write to: Consumer Information Center
Pueblo, CO 81009

discover america — send for free tourist packets

Whether you are planning a family trip or you are just curious about your country, you'll want to send for these state and city tourism packets.

Every state will send you something special. You might get a big fold-out on Arizona history. Or a booklet of colorful photos from Florida.

Most states will send you a road map. Maps tell you many different things about places without using many words. Every map has a "key" to help you read it. The key explains the different map symbols for highways, streets and roads, for big cities, small towns and state capitals.

Cities will also send you information. If you want to know more about the cities in this list, send a request for tourism information to the cities that interest you the most.

directions: Use a postcard.

ask for: Tourist Information Packet

write to: State or City Tourist Information Office of your choice. You'll find the addresses in the following list.

Alabama
Bureau of Publicity and
    Information
403 State Highway Building
Montgomery, AL 36130

Birmingham
Greater Birmingham Convention
    and Visitor's Bureau
Suite 940,
First Alabama Bank Bldg.
Birmingham, AL 35203

Alaska
Division of Tourism
State of Alaska
Pouch E
Juneau, AK 99811

Anchorage
Anchorage Convention and
    Visitor's Bureau
Plaza 201, East Third Avenue
Anchorage, AK 99501

Arizona
Arizona State Office of Tourism
1700 W. Washington
Phoenix, AZ 85007

Phoenix
Phoenix and Valley of the Sun
    Convention & Visitor's Bureau
2701 E. Camelback Road
Phoenix, AZ 85016

Arkansas
Tourism Division
Arkansas Department of Parks
    and Tourism
149 State Capitol Building
Little Rock, AR 72201

Little Rock
Bureau for Conventions and
    Visitors
P.O. Box 3232
Little Rock, AR 72203

California
Office of Visitor Services
Department of Economic and
    Business Development
1120 N Street
Sacramento, CA 95814

Los Angeles
Los Angeles Convention &
    Visitor's Bureau
P.O. Box 71608
Los Angeles, CA 90071

San Diego
San Diego Convention &
    Visitor's Bureau
1200 Third Avenue, Suite 824
San Diego, CA 92101

San Francisco
San Francisco Convention &
    Visitor's Bureau
1390 Market Street, Suite 260
San Francisco, CA 94102

Colorado
Travel Marketing Section
Colorado Division of Commerce
    and Development
1313 Sherman St., Room 500
Denver, CO 80203

Denver
Denver and Colorado
    Convention and Visitor's
    Bureau
225 West Colfax Avenue
Denver, CO 80202

Connecticut
Tourism Division
Connecticut Department of
    Commerce
210 Washington Street
Hartford, CT 06106

Delaware
Delaware State Visitors Service
Division of Economic
    Development
630 State College Road
Dover, DE 19901

District of Columbia
Washington Area Convention
    and Visitor's Association
1129 20th Street, N.W.
Washington, D.C. 20036

Florida
Division of Tourism
Florida Department of
    Commerce
107 West Gaines Street
Tallahassee, FL 32304

Jacksonville
Jacksonville Convention and
    Visitor's Bureau
133 W. Monroe Street
Jacksonville, FL 32207

Miami
Miami Metro Department of
    Publicity and Tourism
499 Biscayne Boulevard
Miami, FL 33132

Georgia
Tourist Division
Bureau of Industry and Trade
P.O. Box 1776
Atlanta, GA 30301

Atlanta
Atlanta Convention and Visitor's
  Bureau
229 Peachtree Street, N.E.
Suite 1414
Atlanta, GA 30303

Hawaii
Hawaii Visitor's Bureau
P.O. Box 8527
Honolulu, HI 96815

Honolulu
Hawaii Visitor's Bureau
P.O. Box 8527
Honolulu, Hi 96815

Idaho
Division of Tourism and
  Industrial Development
State Capitol Building, Rm 108
Boise, ID 83720

Illinois
Illinois Adventure Center
Office of Tourism
160 N. LaSalle
Chicago, IL 60601

Chicago
Chicago Convention and
  Tourism Bureau, Inc.
332 S. Michigan Avenue, Rm 2050
Chicago, IL 60604

Indiana
Tourism Development Division
Indiana Department of
  Commerce
State House, Room 336
Indianapolis, IN 46204

Indianapolis
Indianapolis Convention and
  Visitor's Bureau
100 S. Capitol Avenue
Indianapolis, IN 46225

Iowa
Travel Development Division
Iowa Development Commission
250 Jewett Building
Des Moines, IA 50309

Kansas
Tourist Division
Kansas Department of
  Economic Development
503 Kansas Avenue
Topeka, KS 66603

Kentucky
Division of Advertising and
  Travel Promotion
Department of Public
  Information
Capitol Annex
Frankfort, KY 40601

Louisville
Louisville Visitor's Bureau
300 West Liberty
Louisville, KY 40202

Louisiana
Louisiana Tourist Development
  Commission
P.O. Box 44291, Capitol Station
Baton Rouge, LA 70804

New Orleans
Greater New Orleans Tourist
  Convention Commission
334 Royal Street
New Orleans, LA 70130

Maine
State Development Office
State House
Augusta, ME 04333

Portland
Tourism and Convention Bureau
Greater Portland Chamber of
  Commerce
142 Free Street
Portland, ME 04101

Maryland
Division of Tourist Development
Department of Economic and
  Community Development
1748 Forest Drive
Annapolis, MD 21401

Baltimore
Baltimore Promotion Council,
  Inc.
22 Light Street, Suite 502
Baltimore, MD 21202

Massachusetts
Division of Tourism
Massachusetts Department of
  Commerce and Development
100 Cambridge Street
13th Floor, Government Center
Boston, MA 02202

Boston
Greater Boston Convention and
  Tourist Bureau, Inc.
900 Boylston Street
Boston, MA 02115

Michigan
Travel Bureau
Michigan Department of
  Commerce
P.O. Box 30226
Lansing, MI 48909

Detroit
Metropolitan Detroit Convention
and Visitor's Bureau
100 Rennaisance Center,
Suite 1950
Detroit, MI 48243

Minnesota
Tourism Division
Minnesota Department of
Economic Development
480 Cedar Street, Hanover Bldg.
St. Paul, MN 55101

Mississippi
Travel, Tourism and Public
Affairs Department
Mississippi Agricultural and
Industrial Board
P.O. Box 849
Jackson, MS 39205

Natchez
Natchez Adams County
Chamber of Commerce
P.O. Box 725
Natchez, MS 39120

Missouri
Missouri Division of Tourism
P.O. Box 1055
Jefferson City, MO 65101

Kansas City
Convention and Visitor's Bureau
of Greater Kansas City
1221 Baltimore, Eleventh Floor
Kansas City, MO 64105

St. Louis
Convention and Visitor's Bureau
of Greater St. Louis
500 North Broadway, Suite 1545
St. Louis, MO 63102

Montana
Travel Promotion Unit
Montana Department of
Highways
Helena, MT 59601

Nebraska
Division of Travel and Tourism
Nebraska Department of
Economic Development
P.O. Box 94666
Lincoln, NB 68509

Omaha
Omaha Convention and Visitor's
Council
1620 Dodge Street
Suite 2100
Omaha, NB 68102

Nevada
Travel-Tourism Division
Nevada Department of
Economic Development
Capitol Complex
Carson City, NV 89710

Las Vegas
Convention and Visitor's
Authority
P.O. Box 14006
Las Vegas, NV 89114

New Hampshire
Office of Vacation Travel
Division of Economic
Development
P.O. Box 856
Concord, NH 03301

Manchester
Greater Manchester Chamber of
Commerce
57 Market Street
Manchester, NH 03101

New Jersey
Office of Tourism and Promotion
Department of Labor and
Industry
P.O. Box 400
Trenton, NJ 08625

Atlantic City
Greater Atlantic City Chamber
of Commerce
10 Central Pier
Atlantic City, NJ 08401

New Mexico
Tourist Division
Department of Development
Bataan Memorial Building
Santa Fe, NM 87503

New York
Travel Bureau
New York State Department of
Commerce
99 Washington Avenue
Albany, NY 12245

New York
New York Convention and
Visitor's Bureau, Inc.
90 East 42nd Street
New York, NY 10017

North Carolina
Travel and Tourism Division
North Carolina Department of
Commerce
430 N. Salisbury Street
Raleigh, NC 27611

Charlotte
Convention and Visitor's Bureau
Charlotte Chamber of
Commerce
P.O. Box 1867
Charlotte, NC 28233

North Dakota
North Dakota Travel Division
State Highway Department
Capitol Ground
Bismarck, ND 58505

Ohio
Ohio Office of Travel and
Tourism
Ohio Department of Economic
and Community Development
P.O. Box 1001
Columbus, OH 43216

Cleveland
Cleveland Convention and
Visitor's Bureau, Inc.
511 Terminal Tower
Cleveland, OH 44113

Oklahoma
Tourism Promotion Division
Oklahoma Tourism and
Recreation Department
500 Will Rogers Building
Oklahoma City, OK 73105

Oklahoma City
Oklahoma City Convention and
Tourism
3 Santa Fe Plaza
Oklahoma City, 73102

Oregon
Travel Information Section
101 Transportation Building
Salem, OR 97310

Portland
Convention Bureau and Visitor's
Services
Portland Chamber of Commerce
824 S.W. Fifth Avenue
Portland, OR 97204

Pennsylvania
Bureau of Travel Development
Pennsylvania Department of
Commerce
431 South Office Building
Harrisburg, PA 17120

Philadelphia
Philadelphia Convention and
Visitor's Bureau
1525 John F. Kennedy Blvd.
Philadelphia, PA 19102

Rhode Island
Tourist Promotion Division
Department of Economic
Development
1 Weybosset Hill
Providence, RI 02903

Newport
Convention and Visitor's Bureau
Newport Chamber of Commerce
P.O. Box 237
Newport, RI 02840

South Carolina
Division of Tourism
South Carolina Department of
Parks, Recreation and
Tourism
Room 83, Box 71
Columbia, SC 29202

Charleston
Travel and Convention
Charleston Chamber of
Commerce
P.O. Box 975
Charleston, SC 29402

South Dakota
Department of Economic and
Tourism Development
217 Joe Foss Building
Pierre, SD 57501

Tennessee
Department of Tourist
Development
505 Fesslers Lane
Nashville, TN 37210

Memphis
Convention and Visitor's Bureau
P.O. Box 224
Memphis, TN 38101

Nashville
Convention and Visitor's
Division
Nashville Area Chamber of
Commerce
161 Fourth Avenue, North
Nashville, TN 37219

Texas
Texas Tourist Development
Agency
Box 12008, Capitol Station
Austin, TX 78711

Fort Worth
Fort Worth Area Convention and
Visitor's Bureau
700 Throckmorton Street
Fort Worth, TX 76102

San Antonio
San Antonio Convention and
Visitor's Bureau
P.O. Box 2277
San Antonio, TX 78298

Utah
Utah Travel Council
Council Hall, Capitol Hill
Salt Lake City, UT 84114

Vermont
Vermont Travel Division
Agency of Development and
    Community Affairs
61 Elm Street
Montpelier, VT 05602

Burlington
Lake Champlain Regional
    Chamber of Commerce
P.O. Box 453
Burlington, VT 05401

Virginia
Virginia State Travel Service
6 North Sixth Street
Richmond, VA 23219

Richmond
Convention and Visitor's Bureau
Metropolitan Richmond
    Chamber of Commerce
201 East Franklin Street
Richmond, VA 23219

Washington
Travel Development Division
Department of Commerce and
    Economic Development
General Administration Bldg.
Olympia, WA 98504

Seattle
Seattle-King County Convention
    and Visitor's Bureau
1815 Seventh Avenue
Seattle, WA 98101

West Virginia
Travel Development Division
West Virginia Department of
    Commerce
1900 Washington Street East
Charleston, WV 25305

Wisconsin
Division of Tourism
Department of Business
    Development
123 W. Washington Avenue
Madison, WI 53702

Milwaukee
Greater Milwaukee Convention
    and Visitor's Bureau, Inc.
828 N. Broadway
Milwaukee, WI 53202

Wyoming
Wyoming Travel Commission
I-25 at Etchepare Circle
Cheyenne, WY 82002

Jackson Hole
Jackson Hole Chamber of
    Commerce
P.O. Box E
Jackson Hole, WY 83001

index

You can use this index to quickly find the kinds of items you're most interested in writing away for. So you'll know exactly what you're getting, you should be familiar with some of the terms we use. A **book** or **booklet** measures 6x8 inches or larger. A **pamphlet** is narrower than a book or booklet. A **folder** or **foldout** is one sheet of paper folded up. A **catalog** lists items that you can order by mail. (Most catalog items cost money.)